THE JOY OF
CHRISTMAS

THE JOY OF CHRISTMAS

A Selection of Carols

by

EDWARD HEATH

New York   Oxford University Press   1978

To the members of 'Our Carol Party'
whose joy in singing these carols brings so much
pleasure to others each Christmastide

Library of Congress Cataloging in Publication Data

Main entry under title:
The Joy of Christmas.
With piano acc.
1. Carols. 2. Christmas music. I. Heath, Edward.
M2065.J76   [M5400] 783.6′55′2   78–16540
ISBN 0-19-520080-2
First Printing September 1978
Second Printing November 1978

First published in Great Britain 1977 by
Sidgwick & Jackson Ltd,
in association with
EMI Music Publishing Ltd,
Introduction and text © 1977 by Dumpton Gap Company
Music arrangements © 1977 by EMI Music Publishing Ltd
and see individual copyrights and acknowledgments
Design © 1977 by Sidgwick & Jackson Ltd and EMI Music Publishing Ltd
Designed by Paul Watkins
Picture research by Philippa Lewis
Piano editing by Cecil Bolton and Roy Slack

Printed in the United States of America

Contents

Carols are listed alphabetically both by title (shown in bold) and by first lines

Acknowledgements

The Publishers acknowledge with thanks the following copyright owners who have kindly given permission for reproduction of carols in this book:

Oxford University Press
Rocking: Melody collected and arranged by Martin Shaw (adapted by permission). Words translated by Percy Dearmer
The Birds: Melody collected by Martin Shaw. Words translated by Percy Dearmer
Poverty: Words translated by K. E. Roberts
Song of the Crib: Words translated by Percy Dearmer
The Crown of Roses: Words translated by Geoffrey Dearmer
Unto Us a Boy is Born: Words translated by Percy Dearmer
Zither Carol: Melody arranged by Malcolm Sargent (adapted by permission). Words translated by Malcolm Sargent
Born Today is the Child Divine (Il Est Ne): Words translated by E. T. Chapman
The carols marked * are from The Oxford Book of Carols

G. Schirmer
Jesus Jesus Rest Your Head: Collected by John Jacob Niles
I Wonder as I Wander: Collected by John Jacob Niles

Mrs Ralph Vaughan Williams
The Sussex Carol: Collected by Ralph Vaughan Williams
Gloucestershire Wassail: Collected by Ralph Vaughan Williams

Evans Bros. Ltd.
Infant Holy: Words translated by Edith M. Reed

Novello & Co., Ltd.
The Twelve Days of Christmas: Melody arranged by Frederick Austin (adapted by permission)

Union of Welsh Independents
Poverty: Music by Dr. Caradog Roberts

The Publishers also acknowledge with thanks the following sources who have kindly given permission for reproduction of the illustrations used in this book

Jacket illustration: Detail of Angel Choir by S. Marmion (National Gallery, London)
Page
1 Engraving of carol singers, 1863. (Mary Evans Picture Library)
2 Angel by Melozzo da Forli, St. Peter's, Rome (Mansell Collection)
7 Victorian engraved decoration (Mary Evans Picture Library)
8/9 'The Country Carol Seller' by C. Bede, 1869 (Mary Evans Picture Library)
11 Woodcut of the Adoration of the Magi by A. Durer (Mary Evans Picture Library)
13 Sculpture of Angels from S. Bernardino, Perugia (Mansell Collection)
15 Illuminated initial from 14th century Sienese manuscript (Mansell Collection)
17 18th century bible illustration (Mary Evans Picture Library)
19 Engraved illustration to 19th century carol book (Mansell Collection)
20/21 Woodcuts of the Cuckoo, Wild Pigeon and Ring Dove Vol. I of 'British Birds' by T. Bewick, 1826
21 Virgin and Child, detail of a painting by C. Crivelli, Galleria Brera, Milan (Mansell Collection)
23 Part of the Wilton Diptych, French School c. 1395 (National Gallery, London)
27 16th century engraving of the Adoration of the Shepherds (Mansell Collection)

28/29 Illustrations to 'Good King Wenceslaus' by A. J. Gaskin, 1894 (Mansell Collection and Carter Nash Cameron Ltd.)
31 Victorian decorative border (Elm Tree Books)
33 Victorian engraved decoration (Elm Tree Books)
35 'Christmas at Home,' 19th century engraving (Mary Evans Picture Library)
36 Virgin and Child by Carlo Dolci (National Gallery, London)
39 Head of Christ by Master of Liesborn (National Gallery, London)
41 Woodcut of the Virgin and Child by A. Durer (Mary Evans Picture Library)
43 Adoration of the Shepherds by N. Poussin (National Gallery, London)
45 Massacre of the Innocents, French 18th century engraving (Mansell Collection)
47 'Spirit of Christmas' by R. Seymour, 1836 (Mansell Collection)
49 Angel announcing the Birth of Christ to the Shepherds, French medieval drawing (Mansell Collection)
51 Victorian engraved decoration (Mary Evans Picture Library)
55 'Christmas Gambols and 12th Night's Amusements', early 19th century broadsheet (Fotomas)
57 'Churchgoing on Christmas Morning,' Illustrated London News, 1846 (Mary Evans Picture Library)
59 Virgin and Child, details of painting by A. Verrochio (National Gallery, London)
61 'Christmas Bells', 19th century engraving (Mansell Collection)
63 Adoration of the Magi by A. Durer (Mary Evans Picture Library)
65 'The Star in the East' by H. Warren (Mary Evans Picture Library)
67 Detail of The Nativity by Piero della Francesca (National Gallery, London)
69 The Nativity by Geertgen (National Gallery, London)
71 The Adoration of the Shepherds by D. Ghirlandaio (Mansell Collection)
72 Late 19th century engraving (Mary Evans Picture Library)
72 'The Bow Bell Peal of Christmas Eve', Illustrated London News, 1850 (Mansell Collection)
75 The Nativity, 17th century engraving (Mansell Collection)
77 Bethlehem by W. H. Bartlett (Mary Evans Picture Library)
79 Anonymous early woodcut of the Nativity (Mansell Collection)
81 'Christmas Mummers' by R. Seymour, 1836 (Mansell Collection)
83 Assumption of the Virgin, detail of painting by Matteo di Giovanni (National Gallery, London)
85 Adoration of the Shepherds, detail of painting by Ercole Roberti (National Gallery, London)
87 Illustration to 'I Saw Three Ships' by Willebeek Le Mair (Mary Evans Picture Library)
89 Engraving by M. Schongauer of the Adoration of the Magi British Museum (Fotomas)
91 'Christmas Waits in the Country' Illustrated London News, 1850 (Mary Evans Picture Library)
93 Fresco by Taddeo Gaddi of the Angel Appearing to the Shepherds, S. Croce, Florence (Mansell Collection)
95 19th century engraving of Bethlehem (Mary Evans Picture Library)
96 19th century engraving of Christmas carollers (Mansell Collection)

Introduction

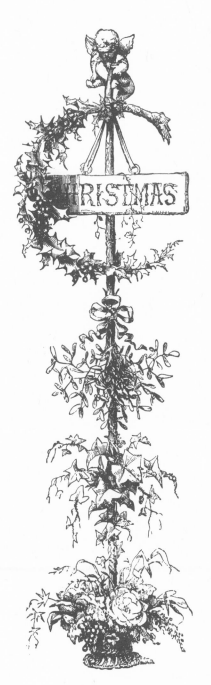

I have always enjoyed Christmas; not just Christmas Day itself, for that passes all too quickly, but the weeks leading up to it culminating in the celebrations of Christ's birth. Some dismiss this as the exploitation and commercialisation of a sacred occasion. For me it is the gradual spread of the spirit of Christmas amongst our friends and neighbours, marked almost everywhere by the singing of carols.

No ceremony, religious or secular, has inspired more music than Christmas. Folk songs, dances, chorales, oratorios, opera and ballet, to say nothing of pantomime, have all contributed. The Easter festival may be more dramatic and full of splendour, Ascension Day and Whitsun more mysterious, but it is Christmas which is human and homely because a baby's birth is within the experience and understanding of us all.

Carols give Christmas its characteristic feeling. They tell the story of the birth of the babe of Bethlehem in a multitude of ways. Their tunes come from almost every country in Europe for they spring from some of the oldest and deepest roots of European civilisation. Others, often folk tunes with their own particular flavour, have since been added from the new world. Together they provide us with a constant source of enjoyment at this festival time. When, as a boy, I first started singing carols, it was a very personal affair. It was only through the efforts of wandering carol parties or in churches that carols could be heard. Today radio and television bring them to our ears in massive profusion; but there is still a place for them to be sung by all of us at Christmas in the home.

My earliest memories of singing carols are round the piano in my grandmother's sitting room. We all went to my grandparents for Christmas dinner in the middle of the day. After the plum pudding had disappeared and the little silver threepenny pieces had been sucked clean, we went into the sitting room to sing. My brother and I had already opened our presents at home as soon as we were awake. These could not be allowed to wait for the family gathering; and if there was anything amongst them for us to wear, it had to be put on for the family to see at Christmas dinner. Instead of gathering round the Christmas tree or listening to the Queen's speech—there were no royal broadcasts in those days—we persuaded one of my aunts to sit at the piano and lead us in carols.

We clamoured for the familiar ones which we had sung at school or heard from carollers on the streets. 'Good King Wenceslas' was the firm favourite, followed by 'The First Nowell'. Other carols we treated on their merits; 'Christians Awake, Salute the Happy Morn' for instance had little appeal to us—it is certainly a magnificent hymn but it may be that there are just too many verses. On the other hand, Mendelssohn's splendid tune for 'Hark! the Herald Angels Sing' always made a great impression and perhaps induced the lustiest singing of any. After these carols, the family usually wanted a few ballads sung by my father or one of my uncles, 'In an Old Fashioned Town' or 'Passing By', songs with nothing whatever to do with our celebrations but old-established favourites. We always finished with three verses of 'O Come All Ye Faithful' before sitting down all too soon to tea and a feast of Christmas cake.

Soon afterwards I became a chorister at the parish church in our small seaside town and when I was ten I was invited to join 'Our Carol Party'. This was a group of enthusiasts who sang unaccompanied carols around the town to collect money to help the children in our convalescent homes. Broadstairs is known for its bracing air. Among others, Queen Victoria stayed there with her mother in her early years and Charles Dickens went there to seek peace and seclusion for writing a number of his books. The children came from London hospitals to recover from a variety of ailments but in particular from tuberculosis. In 'Our Carol Party' I was needed to sing the treble part of the page in 'Good King Wenceslas'. I was also given the job of carrying the ancient lantern with the lighted candle inside and proffering the box to collect contributions. I suspect the carollers hoped my innocent looking young face would wheedle more than the grown-ups out of those whose grand homes we visited.

In October each year 'Our Carol Party' used to foregather after church or chapel on Sunday evenings to practise. Not that we were based on any particular religious denomination. We were not, but at that time most people with good voices liked to be singing in some choir or other on Sundays. We sat round the piano in our organiser's small sitting room. The piano was only used to give us the starting chord or to play over a new carol, for we were especially proud of our unaccompanied singing. We existed to show how carols should be sung as well as to raise money for charity. As we numbered around twenty-four or twenty-five, it was a tight fit in that front room. Some members ended up by sitting on the floor, but that only enhanced the camaraderie which stood us in good stead once we faced the Christmas weather outside. On the North Foreland, slapping our arms across our bodies to keep our circulation going, we could remain cheerful with many a joke about what had happened during our practices on Sunday evenings.

In 'Our Carol Party' I first learnt some of the less well-known carols in this book. The Coventry Carol from the fifteenth century, so difficult to keep in pitch; 'In Dulce Jubilo' with the last verse sung to Bach's thrilling harmonisation; 'Rocking' from Czechoslovakia; and 'When the Crimson Sun Had Set' to its enchanting French tune, which rapidly became known as our opening chorus.

Singing to our neighbours and friends began some three weeks before Christmas. Four hours a night every day of the week except Sundays ensured that we really were singing well. More and more as we went round, we felt the spirit of Christmas growing. For me, as a boy, there was one other great thrill. As the money came rolling in, we were able to plan the presents for the children in the convalescent homes. Being the same age as they were, I was asked to take part in the shopping expeditions. This itself broadened and intensified my feeling about Christmas. The climax came on the afternoon of Christmas Day when I went round to the homes with other members of 'Our Carol Party' to present these Christmas gifts. This made our efforts seem doubly worthwhile. We had enjoyed ourselves singing Christmas carols and we had brought some special Christmas cheer to others.

In my first term at Oxford I discovered the Town Carol Concert. This was held on the last Sunday before Christmas in the Town Hall where the choir and orchestra, the Mayor and Corporation, town and gown all joined together to express the community's common delight in Christmas. An innovation as far as I was concerned was that the audience were taught to sing new carols, some contemporary, others which had only recently come into circulation. I thought that I could not do better than organise a similar Christmas concert in my own small town of Broadstairs, not of course with the same massive resources as the City of Oxford could muster, but using 'Our Carol Party' as the basis of the choir and by collecting together a number of string-playing friends to form the orchestra.

The Chairman of the Council gave his approval to this rather presumptuous initiative by a young student and said he would attend together with his colleagues and their families. On the chosen Sunday afternoon the hall was packed. I taught them how to sing popular carols properly; I introduced one which was new to most of the audience, 'Unto us a Boy is Born' which appears in this book. The sale of programmes and the collection gave us a considerable additional sum with which to help the children. In recent years we have included the old folks' homes as well. Everyone agreed the concert had been a success. It gave our community a feeling of comradeship and unity. With the exception of the Second World War, the Broadstairs Town Carol Concerts have taken place every Christmas for the last forty years. Their existence is now well-known because of their appearance on radio and television. I have conducted them all with the exception of 1973 when, as Prime Minister, I was unable to return from the European Summit Conference in Copenhagen in time for the concert. Thousands of people have enjoyed singing and listening to carols in this way.

I know, however, that there are many other occasions when people would like to be able to sing carols together as part of their Christmas celebrations but all too often they have no music or words available. The pianist rather inadequately strums a half-improvised accompaniment to words which rapidly degenerate into a series of mumblings. As a result the occasion loses its natural spontaneity and zest. I have brought together in this book a wide variety of carols, including some from the Town Carol Concert, arranged so that they can be sung in unison and with interesting piano accompaniments which should not prove too difficult for the pianist who has to sight read at a Christmas party. Of course, the old favourites are here, but I have added a number of the lesser known ones which I hope will bring pleasure to young and old alike.

It is a joy to listen to carols which are well sung; for most of us it is an even greater joy to be able to take some part in singing them ourselves. In our choirs and choral societies up and down the land, at school services or end of term concerts, at festivities in the pubs and clubs, in carol parties on the streets, or at home with the family singing round the piano in the sitting room, they enable us to express our feelings of delight at Christmas and to share in its joy. May this book year by year help us to experience more fully, each in our own way, the celebration of Christ's birth.

The First Nowell

This, probably the best known of all Christmas carols, is the one with which we always open our Town Carol Concert at Broadstairs, my home town by the sea on the most south-easterly tip of England. This carol is thought to have been written not later than the 17th century, although the version we usually sing dates from early in the 19th century. We take it fairly briskly to avoid a plodding effect and we give it some rhythmic bounce by emphasising the phrasing, particularly in the chorus. To make some contrasts, the ladies can sing verses 2 and 4 and the men verses 3 and 5. Everyone should join together to sing the first and last verses.

Traditional

was so deep. Now-ell, Now-ell, Now-ell, Now-
D A7 D A7 D Bm F♯ D G

-ell,____ Born is the King_ of Is - ra - el.
D A Bm D G D G A7 D A7 D

2. They lookèd up and saw a Star,
   Shining in the East, beyond them far,
   And to the earth it gave great light,
   And so it continued both day and night.
   Nowell, etc.

3. And by the light of that same Star,
   Three Wise Men came from country far;
   To seek for a King was their intent,
   And to follow the Star wherever it went.
   Nowell, etc.

4. This star drew nigh to the north-west,
   O'er Bethlehem it took its rest,
   And there it did both stop and stay,
   Right over the place where Jesus lay.
   Nowell, etc.

5. Then entered in those Wise Men three,
   Full reverently upon their knee,
   And offered there, in His Presence,
   Their gold, and myrrh, and frankincense.
   Nowell, etc.

6. Then let us all with one accord,
   Sing praises to our Heavenly Lord,
   That hath made Heaven and earth of nought,
   And with His Blood mankind hath bought.
   Nowell, etc.

In Dulci Jubilo

This glorious German melody is to be found on a 14th century manuscript in Leipzig University. The theme has been arranged in a variety of ways. One of the simplest is that of Bartholomew Gesius of 1601; the most splendid is the setting by Johann Sebastian Bach; the most beautiful, the harmonisation by R. L. de Pearsall for choir and vocal quartet; and the most horrible the one to the words customarily pronounced 'Good Christian men rejoi-i-oice' which I was made to sing as a chorister.
This is a 'macaronic' carol, that is to say the words are a mixture of English (translated from the German) and dog Latin.

From the 14th Century German

2. *O Jesu, parvule,*
   For thee I long alway;
     Comfort my heart's blindness,
   O puer optime,
     With all thy loving-kindness,
   O princeps gloriae.
   Trahe me post te!

3. *O Patris caritas!*
   O Nati lenitas!
     Deeply were we stainèd
   Per nostra crimina;
     But thou for us hast gainèd
   Coelorum gaudia.
   O that we were there!

4. *Ubi sunt gaudia*
   In any place but there?
     There are angels singing
   Nova cantica,
     And there the bells are ringing
   In Regis curia.
   O that we were there!

Away in a Manger

Christmas is a time above all for children and this carol is one especially for them. Children's voices give it a character all its own. No one knows who wrote the words, but the tune, so easy for children to remember, is by a 19th century composer, W. J. Kirkpatrick. It is most effective when sung with expression but without sentimentality.

Anonymous

W. J. Kirkpatrick

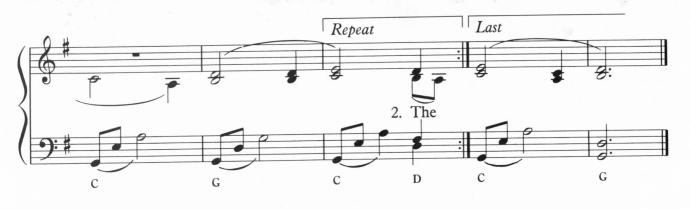

2. The cattle are lowing, the baby awakes,
   But little Lord Jesus no crying he makes,
   I love thee, Lord Jesus, look down from the sky,
   And stay by my side until morning is nigh.

3. Be near me, Lord Jesus, I ask thee to stay
   Close by me for ever, and love me, I pray:
   Bless all the dear children in thy tender care,
   And fit us for heaven, to live with thee there.

While Shepherds Watched

When small boys appear on the doorstep around Christmas Eve plaintively wailing a carol, the chances are that this is the one their untuned voices will attempt to produce. It deserves a better fate.

Its words go back to 1700. Then they were sung to a jolly and bouncing tune much more characteristic of a carol than the one we now use, even though this is older and dates from 1592. In singing it we have to pay particular attention to the words of the 5th verse; it needs a deep breath to sing 'And forthwith appeared a shining throng of Angels praising God' without interrupting it and thus spoiling the sense.

Nahum Tate

Este's Psalter (1592)

★To be applied to selected verses.

2. "Fear not," said he; For mighty dread
   Had seized their troubled mind;
   "Glad tidings of great joy I bring
   To you and all mankind."

3. "To you in David's town this day
   Is born of David's line
   A Saviour, Who is Christ the Lord;
   And this shall be the sign:"

4. "The heavenly Babe you there shall find
   To human view display'd,
   All meanly wrapp'd in swathing bands,
   And in a manger laid."

5. Thus spake the seraph; and forthwith
   Appear'd a shining throng
   Of Angels praising God, who thus
   Address'd their joyful song:

6. "All glory be to God on high,
   And to the earth be peace;
   Good-will henceforth from heaven to men
   Begin and never cease."

Fear not, for Behold, I bring you good tidings of Great Joy, which shall be to all people. Luke II—10.

Sussex Carol

(On Christmas Night)

This traditional carol from the south of England was collected by Ralph Vaughan Williams. It has an emphatic rhythm which carries everything along before it.

For many years I wanted the audience at our Town Carol Concert to be able to sing this with an orchestral accompaniment, but I was reluctant to attempt it. When I did finally summon up the courage to teach it to them, I found a surprisingly ready response. They had heard the choir sing it many times before and they sounded as though they had been genuinely wanting to sing it for a long time. In fact, the carol had created its own support. It must be the mark of a real folk tune when people want to join in.

Traditional collected Ralph Vaughan Williams

1. On Christ-mas night all Christ-ians sing, To hear the news the an-gels bring. On Christ-mas night all Christ-ians sing, To hear the news the an-gels bring; News of great joy news of great mirth, News of our mer-ci-ful King's birth.

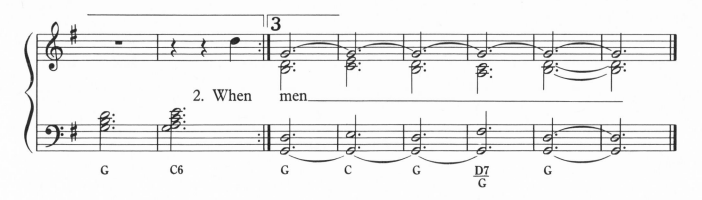

2. When men

G C6 G C G D7/G G

2. When sin departs before Thy grace,
   Then life and health come in its place; } *Repeat twice*
   Angels and men with joy may sing,
   All for to see the new-born King.

3. All out of darkness we have light,
   Which made the angels sing this night; } *Repeat twice*
   "Glory to God and peace to men,
   Now and for evermore. Amen."

The Birds

This delightful Czech carol is much less well known than 'Rocking', which follows later in this book. It was taken down from a peasant girl singing it some fifty years ago. The words have an attractiveness all of their own. The music of the birds' songs at the end of each verse brings the carol to a delicate but clear conclusion.

Translation O.B.C.

Czech Carol collected Martin Shaw

From out of a wood did a Cuc-koo fly, cuc-koo, He came to a man-ger with joy-ful cry, Cuc-koo, He hopped, he curt-sied,

round he flew, And loud his ju - bi - la - tion

D11   D7   A7   G   A7   D11

D. 𝄋

grew, Cuc - koo, cuc - koo, cuc - koo. _____

D7   Gmaj7   Am7   D   C   G

2. A pigeon flew over to Galilee,
        Vrercroo,
    He strutted and cooed, and was full of glee,
        Vrercroo,
    And showed with jewelled wings unfurled,
    His joy that Christ was in the world,
        Vrercroo, vrercroo, vrercroo.

3. A dove settled down upon Nazareth,
        Tsucroo,
    And tenderly chanted with all his breath
        Tsucroo:
    'O you,' he cooed, 'so good and true,
    My beauty do I give to you—'
        Tsucroo, tsucroo, tsucroo.

Hark! The Herald Angels Sing

This has long been one of the most popular of the Christmas hymns, but all too often it is cheapened in its performance. Mendelssohn wrote a stately tune, full of dignity and splendour. We need to sing it at a steady pace with rounded tone, otherwise it becomes trivial.

Charles Wesley

Mendelssohn

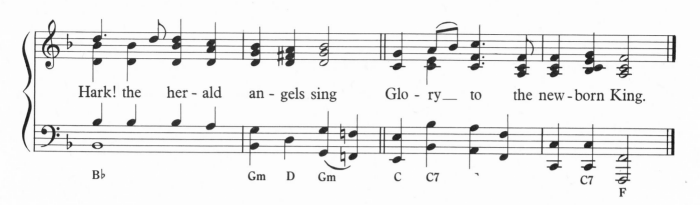

Hark! the her-ald an-gels sing Glo-ry — to the new-born King.

B♭ Gm D Gm C C7 C7 F

2. Christ, by highest heaven adored,
Christ, the everlasting Lord,
Late in time behold him come,
Offspring of a Virgin's womb,
Veiled in flesh the Godhead see!
Hail, the incarnate Deity!
Pleased as Man with man to dwell,
Jesus, our Emmanuel.
   Hark! the herald angels sing
   Glory to the new-born King.

3. Hail, the heaven-born Prince of Peace!
Hail, the Sun of Righteousness,
Light and life to all he brings,
Risen with healing in his wings.
Mild he lays his glory by,
Born that man no more may die,
Born to raise the sons of earth,
Born to give them second birth.
   Hark! the herald angels sing
   Glory to the new-born King.

Whence is that Goodly Fragrance

This is a more elaborate French traditional carol usually heard as a four-part song. It was in this form that I first conducted it as a boy of sixteen or seventeen at a competitive music festival. It has such a beautiful flowing line that it is a delight to sing. It deserves to be heard more often at Christmastide. The tune is a fine example of adaptability in music. It reappeared as a rousing drinking song 'Fill every glass, for wine inspires us' in *The Beggar's Opera* in the 18th century.

Translation A. B. Ramsay

Old French Carol

1. Whence is that good-ly fra-grance flow-ing, Steal-ing our sens-es all a-way?____ Nev-er the like did come a-

2. What is that light so brilliant, breaking
   Here in the night across our eyes?
   Never so bright the day-star waking
   Started to climb the morning skies!
   What is that light so brilliant, breaking
   Here in the night across our eyes?

3. Bethlehem! there in manger lying
   Find your Redeemer, haste away!
   Run ye with eager footsteps hieing!
   Worship the Saviour born to-day!
   Bethlehem! there in manger lying
   Find your Redeemer, haste away!

Song of the Crib

The manuscript of this 15th century German tune is in Leipzig University. Like so many of the early carols, it was intended to be sung as part of a Mystery Play which in this case would have been acted around the crib inside the church.

It has a soft, lilting rhythm beautifully suited to a cradle song and the tune has the utmost simplicity.

Translation N.S.T.

From the 15th Century German

Men shall bring him from far and wide Love's di - a - dem; Je - sus,

Eb   Fm7   Bb11 Bb7 Eb   Gm   Cm

Je - sus, Lo, he comes, and Love's and saves, and frees us!

Gm   Cm   Ab   Gm   Fm   Bb11 Bb7 Ab   Eb

2. Gladly, dear one, lady mine,
   Help I cradle this child of thine;
   God's own light on us both shall shine
       In Paradise,
           As prays the mother Mary.

   Chorus:
   He came among us at Christmas tide,
       At Christmas tide,
           In Bethlehem;
   Men shall bring him from far and wide
           Love's diadem:
       Jesus, Jesus,
   Lo, he comes, and loves, and saves, and
                   [frees us!

3. *Servant* (1)
   Peace to all that have goodwill!
   God, who heaven and earth doth fill,
   Comes to turn us away from ill,
       And lies so still
           Within the crib of Mary.

4. *Servant* (2)
   All shall come and bow the knee;
   Wise and happy their souls shall be,
   Loving such a divinity,
       As all may see
           In Jesus, Son of Mary.

5. *Servant* (3)
   Now is born Emmanuel,
   Prophesied once by Ezekiel,
   Promised Mary by Gabriel—
       Ah, who can tell
           Thy Praises, Son of Mary!

6. *Servant* (4)
   Thou my lazy heart hast stirred,
   Thou, the Father's eternal Word,
   Greater than aught that ear hath heard,
       Thou tiny bird
           Of love, thou Son of Mary.

Good King Wenceslas

This tune was originally used as a Spring carol and as such it was included in a collection of 1582. It was not until the middle of the 19th century that the legend of Good King Wenceslas was recounted in the words which we now use for this carol. Saint Wenceslas (c. 903-935), Duke and Patron of Bohemia, received a Christian education and after the death of his father encouraged Christianity in Bohemia against the wishes of his mother. Noted for his piety he was murdered by his brother Buleslav.

I began singing carols in our carol party when I was a boy as the treble soloist in the part of the page. In my last two lines my voice slowed and faltered dramatically as I sang 'Fails my heart, I know not how, I can go no longer.'

It is natural for us to sing this at the Town Carol Concert just before the appeal for funds is made . . . 'Ye who now will bless the poor, shall yourselves find blessing.'

J. M. Neale

Piae Cantiones (1582)

Good King Wen-ces - las looked out, On the Feast of Ste - phen,

When the snow lay round a - bout, Deep, and crisp, and e - ven:

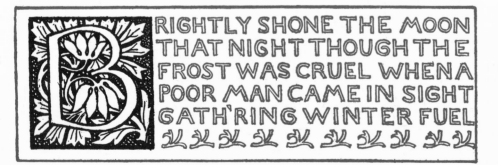

BRIGHTLY SHONE THE MOON THAT NIGHT THOUGH THE FROST WAS CRUEL WHEN A POOR MAN CAME IN SIGHT GATH'RING WINTER FUEL

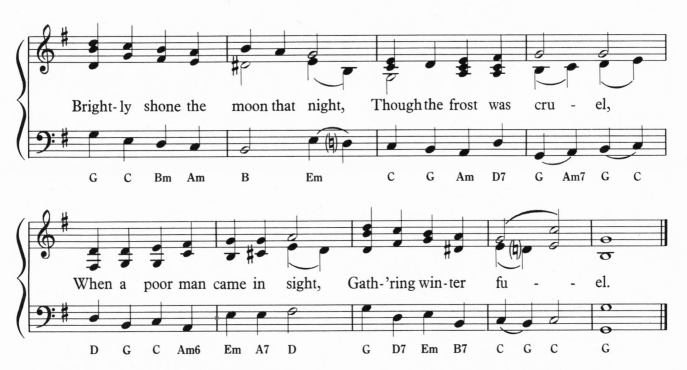

"SIRE THE NIGHT IS DARKER NOW, AND THE WIND BLOWS STRONGER: FAILS MY HEART, I KNOW NOT HOW, I CAN GO NO LONGER." MARK MY FOOTSTEPS, MY GOOD PAGE: TREAD THOU IN THEM BOLDLY, THOU SHALT FIND THE WINTER WIND FREEZE THY BLOOD LESS COLDLY"

PAGE AND MONARCH FORTH THEY WENT. FORTH THEY WENT TOGETHER: THROUGH THE RUDE WINDS LOUD LAMENT AND THE BITTER WEATHER.

Bright-ly shone the moon that night, Though the frost was cru- el,

When a poor man came in sight, Gath-'ring win-ter fu - - el.

2. 'Hither, page, and stand by me,
    If thou know'st it, telling,
Yonder peasant, who is he?
    Where and what his dwelling?'
'Sire, he lives a good league hence,
    Underneath the mountain,
Right against the forest fence,
    By Saint Agnes' fountain.'

3. 'Bring me flesh, and bring me wine,
    Bring me pine-logs hither:
Thou and I will see him dine,
    When we bear them thither.'
Page and monarch, forth they went,
    Forth they went together;
Through the rude wind's wild lament
    And the bitter weather.

4. 'Sire, the night is darker now,
    And the wind blows stronger;
Fails my heart, I know not how;
    I can go no longer.'
'Mark my footsteps, good my page;
    Tread thou in them boldly:
Thou shalt find the winter's rage
    Freeze thy blood less coldly.'

5. In his master's steps he trod,
    Where the snow lay dinted;
Heat was in the very sod
    Which the Saint had printed.
Therefore, Christian men, be sure,
    Wealth or rank possessing,
Ye who now will bless the poor,
    Shall yourselves find blessing.

The Holly and the Ivy

There are many versions of this carol and several charming arrangements of it. In particular that by Sir Walford Davies is most effective. I have included a simple straightforward version here which can easily be sung round the piano.

The words of this carol may well have a pagan origin, in which the male is symbolised by the holly and the female by the ivy. The Romans used holly to decorate houses in the festival of the Saturnalia which occurred at the same season. Ivy is dedicated to Bacchus from the notion that it is a prevention of drunkenness. In Christian symbolism it typifies the everlasting life by remaining constantly green.

We turn the carol into a dialogue by having the women and the men singing verses 2, 3, 4 and 5 alternately.

play-ing of the mer-ry or-gan, Sweet sing-ing in the choir.

F   Bb   F   Db7   F   C7   F

2. The Holly bears a blossom
As white as any flower;
And Mary bore sweet Jesus Christ
To be our sweet Saviour.

*O the rising of the sun
And the running of the deer,
The playing of the merry organ,
Sweet singing in the choir.*

3. The Holly bears a berry
As red as any blood;
And Mary bore sweet Jesus Christ
To do poor sinners good.

4. The Holly bears a prickle
As sharp as any thorn;
And Mary bore sweet Jesus Christ
On Christmas day in the morn.

5. The Holly bears a bark
As bitter as any gall;
And Mary bore sweet Jesus Christ
For to redeem us all.

Masters in This Hall

This magnificent rousing tune is a French traditional carol. The only problem about singing it is that it does cover a wide vocal range, too high for some, too low for others. If they sing out boldly, most people ought to be able to manage it. The words were written by William Morris. The last sentence of the chorus, 'God today hath poor folk raised and cast adown the proud' may appear to some to present a false contrast all too reminiscent of 19th century do-gooding. But we must not let that spoil the whole carol for us.

William Morris

Old French Carol

2. Going o'er the hills;
   Thro' the milk-white snow,
   Heard I ewes bleat
   While the wind did blow.

3. Shepherds many an one
   Sat among the sheep,
   No man spake more word
   Than they had been asleep.

4. Quoth I, "Fellows mine,
   Why this guise sit ye?
   Making but dull cheer
   Shepherds tho' you be?"

5. "Shepherds should of right
   Leap and dance and sing,
   Thus to see ye sit,
   Is a right strange thing."

6. Quoth those fellows then,
   "To Bethlem Town we go,
   To see a Mighty Lord
   Lie in manger low."

7. "How name ye this Lord
   Shepherds?", then said I
   "Very God," they said,
   "Come from Heaven high."

8. Then to Bethlem Town
   We went two and two,
   And in a sorry place
   Heard the oxen low.

9. Therein did we see
   A sweet and goodly May
   And a fair old man,
   Upon the straw She lay.

10. And a little Child
    On Her arm had She
    "Wot ye Who This is?",
    Said the hinds to me.

11. Ox and ass Him know,
    Kneeling on their knee,
    Wondrous joy had I
    This little Babe to see.

12. This is Christ the Lord,
    Masters be ye glad!
    Christmas is come in,
    And no folk should be sad.

We Wish You a Merry Christmas

The most familiar words at Christmas time are set here to a traditional West Country carol. Its rousing words express all the high spirits of the carollers on their rounds. The demand for figgy pudding with the firm declamation that they won't go until they get some, adds a touch of Christmas fare to their greetings. This was a latecomer to our own carolling, but I knew that as soon as we introduced it to our audience at the Town Carol Concert it would become a popular feature. In fact we have had to include it in every programme since our first performance. With the passage of time, it has accumulated its own traditions. It is now inevitably encored and, to give an air of credibility to their words, the choir stops in full spate on the second time round to re-emphasise their demands, no matter what the conductor does to try to induce them to continue. With the appearance of a large figgy pudding in the arms of the white-coated chef, however, they are reassured and finish the carol with a whirlwind of Christmas and New Year greetings.

Traditional West Country

wish you a mer-ry Christ-mas, And a Hap-py New Year.

B   Em   G   C   Am D7 G

2. Now bring us some figgy pudding,
   Now bring us some figgy pudding,
   Now bring us some figgy pudding,
   And bring some out here.

   Good tidings we bring
   To you and your kin,
   We wish you a Merry Christmas,
   And a Happy New Year.

3. For we all like figgy pudding,
   We all like figgy pudding,
   For we all like figgy pudding,
   So bring some out here.

4. And we won't go till we've got some,
   We won't go, till we've got some,
   And we won't go till we've got some,
   So bring some out here.

The Crown of Roses

(The Legend)

Tchaikovsky wrote this in his 'Songs for Young People' in Moscow in 1883 to words by Plechtchéev. The story it tells is appealing in itself, but 'The Legend' is also symbolic of what was to happen to the Christ Child in his lifetime.

It is difficult to think of a less complicated piece to sing; yet it contains all the passion we associate with Russian church music.

Plechtchéev, translated G.D.   P. I. Tchaikovsky

Moderato

1. When Je-sus Christ was yet a child He had a_ gar-den small and wild, Where-in he cher-ished ro-ses fair, And wove them in-to gar-lands there. 2. Now once, as_ sum-mer-time_ drew_ nigh,_ There came a_ troop_ of child-ren_ by,

pressed it ___ down, Till on his fore - head fair and young Red

B7   Em   D   C   D7   G

drops of ___ blood ___ like ro - ses sprung. ___

G#° Am Em   B7   Em

Born Today is the Child Divine

(Il Est Né)

This carol haunted me for many years before I finally managed to track it down. I first heard a short extract of it sung by children in a broadcast from Canada just before the Queen's Christmas message one year. I did not hear it again for several years and it was not until the 1960's that I found an arrangement which we were able to sing at our Carol Concert. It has a memorable quality about it which keeps the tune running through your head long after you have sung it, thanks largely to its dance rhythm. It must have originated in France and thence travelled out to Canada. I never tire of hearing it.

Translation E. T. Chapman

Old French Carol

poco rall. **a tempo**

Child di - vine. Dance and sing this hap - py day. Christ is born the

Am Em Am D G C G C G Em

Son of Ma - ry: Dance and sing all care a - way, Let us all our hom - age pay.

Am D G C G C G Em G Am D7 G

D.C.

2. Christ is come to set us free
   From the curse of sin's dominion,
   From the yoke of tyranny.
   He is come our Lord to be.
   Dance and sing this happy day,
   Christ is born the Son of Mary:
   Dance and sing all care away,
   Let us all our homage pay.
   Ox and ass before Him fall,
   With the shepherds humbly kneeling
   There before the lowly stall,
   There before the Lord of all.

3. Dance and sing this happy day,
   Christ is born the Son of Mary:
   Dance and sing all care away,
   Let us all our homage pay.
   Hail, thou wondrous star so bright,
   In the winter sky appearing,
   Leading on with steadfast light
   Eastern monarchs thro' the night.
   Dance and sing this happy day,
   Christ is born the Son of Mary:
   Dance and sing all care away,
   Let us all our homage pay.

4. Come, thou long expected Son,
   Springing from the stem of Jesse,
   Come, thou ever blessed One,
   Here on earth Thy will be done.
   Dance and sing this happy day,
   Christ is born the Son of Mary:
   Dance and sing all care away,
   Let us all our homage pay.
   Dance and sing this happy day,
   Christ is born the Son of Mary:
   Dance and sing all care away,
   Let us all our homage pay.

God Rest You Merry, Gentlemen

This splendid traditional carol is said to have been sung in the streets of London in the middle of the last century, from a broadsheet printed some fifty years earlier.

'God rest you merry, Gentlemen' means 'God keep you happy, Gentlemen'. This carol will certainly do that if it is sung in a robust and spirited way.

Traditional

God, rest you mer-ry, gen-tle-men, Let no-thing you dis-may, Re-mem-ber Christ our Sa-viour was born on Christ-mas Day, To save us all from Sa-tan's power When we were gone a-stray, O ti-dings of com-fort and joy, com-fort and

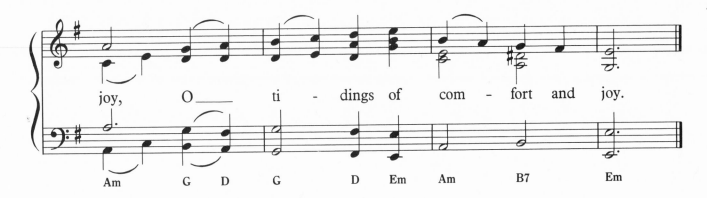

joy,　O＿ti - dings of com - fort and joy.

Am　G　D　G　D　Em　Am　B7　Em

2. In Bethlehem, in Jewry,
　This blessèd Babe was born,
And laid within a manger,
　Upon this blessèd morn;
The which His Mother Mary
　Did nothing take in scorn.
　　　O tidings, etc.

3. From God our Heavenly Father
　A blessed Angel came;
And unto certain Shepherds
　Brought tidings of the same:
How that in Bethlehem was born
　The Son of God by name.
　　　O tidings, etc.

4. "Fear not then," said the Angel,
　"Let nothing you affright,
This day is born a Saviour
　Of a pure Virgin bright,
To free all those that trust in Him
　From Satan's power and might."
　　　O tidings, etc.

5. The shepherds at those tidings
　Rejoicèd much in mind,
And left their flocks a-feeding,
　In tempest, storm, and wind:
And went to Bethlehem straightway,
　The Son of God to find.
　　　O tidings, etc.

6. And when they came to Bethlehem
　Where our dear Saviour lay,
They found Him in a manger,
　Where oxen fed on hay;
His Mother Mary kneeling down,
　Unto the Lord did pray.
　　　O tidings, etc.

7. Now to the Lord sing praises,
　All you within this place,
And with true love and brotherhood
　Each other now embrace;
This holy tide of Christmas
　All other do deface.
　　　O tidings, etc.

Coventry Carol

This is one of the earliest of English carols. I have chosen the original tune of 1591, sung in the Coventry plays from the 16th century onwards. Its sadness is in contrast to the sweetness of the 'Song of the Crib', which appears later in this book, but it characterises the sorrow of the women of Bethlehem, just before King Herod's soldiers arrived to murder their children.

16th Century

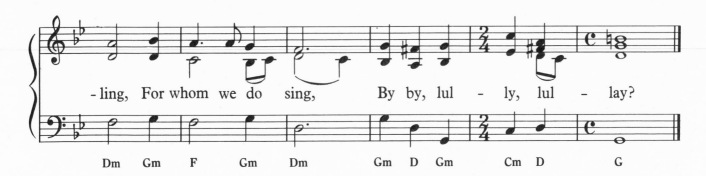

-ling, For whom we do sing, By by, lul - ly, lul - lay?

Dm Gm F Gm Dm Gm D Gm Cm D G

2. Herod, the king,
   In his raging,
     Chargèd he hath this day
   His men of might,
   In his own sight,
     All young childrén to slay.

3. That woe is me,
   Poor child for thee!
     And ever morn and day,
   For thy parting
   Neither say nor sing
     By by, lully, lullay!

Wassail Song

(Here We Come A-wassailing)

'Here We Come A-wassailing' has all the characteristics of a true carol. It is simple and direct. Its lilting rhythm suggests the original dance form of these pieces. It is full of merriment and goodwill—'Love and joy come to you'—and its sentiments are well suited to the occasion.

There are a number of wassail songs—The Gloucestershire Wassail appears later in this collection,—and this one is thought to have originated in Yorkshire. 'Wassail' is a cheery form of greeting meaning 'Keep you well', and the Wassail Cup was a horn from which everyone drank. The Wassail Song is often sung at the New Year as well as at Christmas.

This carol conjures up more vividly than any other the feeling of what it is like to be carolling on people's doorsteps. So topical are the words that we carollers got more fun out of singing this than any other. We certainly were 'neighbours' children whom you have seen before' and although there were not many butlers around, we still chanted 'let him bring us up a glass of beer and better we shall sing'. Needless to say, we were always ready to sink half a pint if one appeared.

It was seldom necessary to urge us to put more emotional feeling into 'Pray think of us poor children who are wandering in the mire'; having splashed our way through the slush on a garden path, we all too often found ourselves up to our ankles in the mud of the flower beds as we gathered round to sing.

Traditional North of England

too, And God bless you, and send you A hap - py new

Eb   Bb7   Eb   Ab   Fm7   Bb7   Eb

year, And God send you A hap - py new year.___

Ab   Abm   Eb   C   Fm7   Eb   Bb7   Eb

2. Our wassail cup is made
   Of the rosemary tree,
And so is your beer
   Of the best barley:

   Love and joy come to you,
   And to you your wassail too,
   And God bless you, and send you
   A happy new year.
   And God send you a happy new year.

3. We are not daily beggars
   That beg from door to door,
But we are neighbours' children
   Whom you have seen before:

4. Call up the butler of this house,
   Put on his golden ring;
Let him bring us up a glass of beer,
   And better we shall sing:

5. We have got a little purse
   Of stretching leather skin;
We want a little of your money
   To line it well within:

6. Bring us out a table,
   And spread it with a cloth;
Bring us out a mouldy cheese
   And some of your Christmas loaf:

7. God bless the master of this house,
   Likewise the mistress too;
And all the little children
   That round the table go:

8. Good Master and good Mistress,
   While you're sitting by the fire,
Pray think of us poor children
   Who are wandering in the mire:

When the Crimson Sun had Set

Popularly known in our carol party as 'The Opening Chorus', this was the first carol we sang when we started on our rounds each evening. The tune is an old French one, more often used for the words 'Angels from the realms of glory, wing your flight o'er all the earth', with its refrain 'Come and worship; worship Christ the new born King'.

This choice put me in something of a dilemma. Should I include the better known, more sophisticated version of the tune or 'The Opening Chorus', which brings back so many memories of my youth? I have decided on the latter for sentimental reasons. It is also simpler to sing and rather more suitable for our parties round the piano at home.

From an Old French Carol

When the crim-son sun had set Low be-hind the win-try sea,
On the bright and cold mid-night Burst a sound of heaven-ly glee:

Glo - ri - a, Glo - ri - a, Glo - - - ri - a,
Glo - - - - - - - - - ri - a

in Ex - cel - sis De - o, Glo - ri - a, Glo - ri - a
in Ex - cel - sis De - o, Glo - - - -

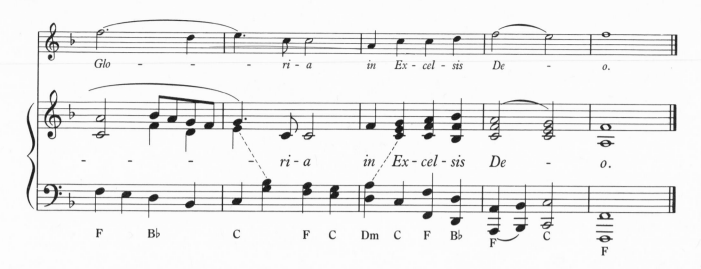

Glo — — — ri - a in Ex - cel - sis De - o.

— — — — ri - a in Ex - cel - sis De - o.

F   B♭   C   F   C   Dm C   F   B♭   F   C   F

2. Shepherds watching by their fold,
   On the crisp and hoary plain,
        In the sky
        Bright Hosts espy,
   Singing in a gladsome strain,
            Gloria, etc.

3. Join with us in welcome song,
   Ye who in Christ's Home abide,
        Sing the Love
        Of God above,
   Shown at happy Christmas-tide.
            Gloria, etc.

The Twelve Days of Christmas

This carol has greatly grown in popularity over the last 25 years. When we first sang it at the Broadstairs Town Carol Concert it was hardly known at all and it took the audience some time to master all its tricks before they could sing it by heart. Since then, it has been performed elsewhere in every conceivable version, crooned, popped, and even hotted up to advertise soft drinks. I have included here a straightforward arrangement for voice and piano.

The tune constantly repeats itself but beware when we reach five gold rings! This carol has to be kept moving but we mustn't rush it—at least not until we get to the twelfth day of Christmas.

Traditional

52

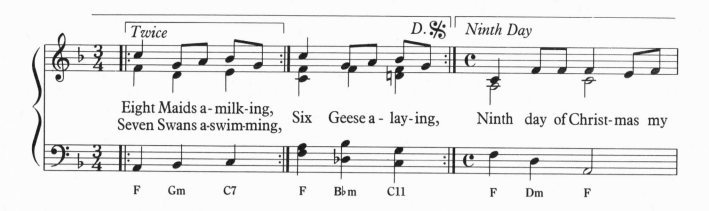

Twice ... *D.S.%* *Ninth Day*

Eight Maids a-milk-ing, Six Geese a-lay-ing, Ninth day of Christ-mas my
Seven Swans a-swim-ming,

F Gm C7 F B♭m C11 F Dm F

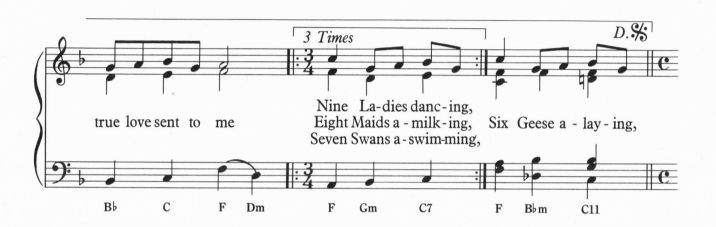

3 Times ... *D.S.%*

true love sent to me Nine La-dies danc-ing,
Eight Maids a-milk-ing, Six Geese a-lay-ing,
Seven Swans a-swim-ming,

B♭ C F Dm F Gm C7 F B♭m C11

Tenth Day ... *4 Times*

Tenth day of Christ-mas my true love sent to me Ten Lords a-leap-ing,
Nine La-dies danc-ing,
Eight Maids a-milk-ing,
Seven Swans a-swim-ming,

F Dm B♭m C7 F Dm F B♭ C7

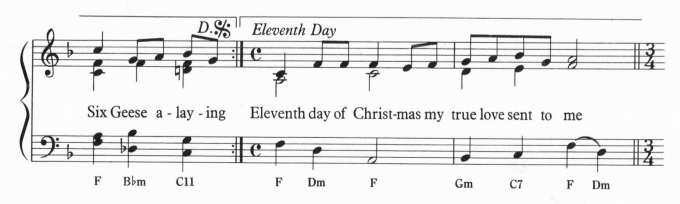

D.S.% *Eleventh Day*

Six Geese a-lay-ing Eleventh day of Christ-mas my true love sent to me

F B♭m C11 F Dm F Gm C7 F Dm

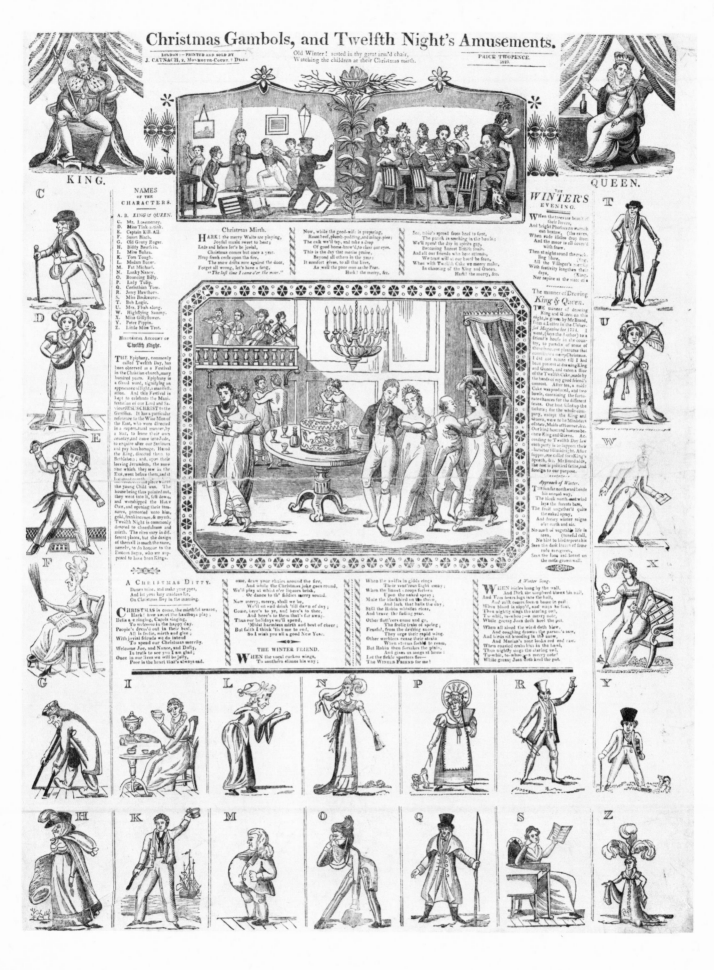

See Amid the Winter's Snow

Another simple 19th century English Christmas hymn, this time written by Sir John Goss, a prolific writer of church music and organist of St Paul's. This provides plenty of opportunities for different members of the group to sing the verses whilst at the same time giving all of us a lusty chorus at the end of each one.

This was particularly popular with us whenever we had a white Christmas. Standing out in the snow on a crisp frosty night, we felt that this picture of the Christmas scene was certainly appropriate for us.

Edward Caswall

John Goss

★To be applied to selected verses.

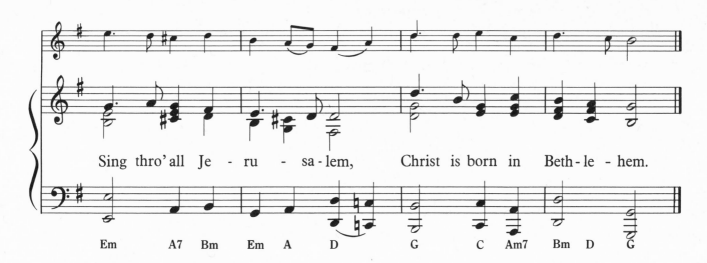

Sing thro' all Je - ru - sa - lem, Christ is born in Beth - le - hem.

Em A7 Bm Em A D G C Am7 Bm D G

2. Lo, within a manger lies
   He who built the starry skies;
   He, who throned in height sublime,
   Sits amid the Cherubim!
      Hail, thou ever-blessed, etc.

3. Say, ye holy Shepherds, say,
   What your joyful news to-day;
   Wherefore have ye left your sheep
   On the lonely mountain steep?
      Hail, thou ever-blessed, etc.

4. "As we watched at dead of night,
   Lo, we saw a wondrous light;
   Angels singing peace on earth,
   Told us of a Saviour's Birth."
      Hail, thou ever-blessed, etc.

5. Sacred Infant, all Divine,
   What a tender love was Thine;
   Thus to come from highest bliss
   Down to such a world as this!
      Hail, thou ever-blessed, etc.

6. Teach, O teach us, Holy Child,
   By Thy face so meek and mild,
   Teach us to resemble Thee,
   In Thy sweet humility!
      Hail, thou ever-blessed, etc.

Rocking

It is surprising how many of our quiet carols originate from Czechoslovakia. This one has the lilting rhythm of a lullaby, the words suiting the accents in the tune to perfection. It is difficult to imagine a simpler, or more effective carol.

Czech Carol collected Martin Shaw

Lit - tle Je - sus, sweet - ly___ sleep, do not___ stir;

We will___ lend you a coat of___ fur, We will rock you,

rock you, rock you, We will rock you, rock you, rock you:

See the fur to keep you__warm, Snug - ly__round your ti - ny__form.

2. Mary's little baby, sleep, sweetly sleep,
  Sleep in comfort, slumber deep;
    We will rock you, rock you, rock you,
    We will rock you, rock you, rock you:
  We will serve you all we can,
  Darling, darling little man.

Christmas Bells

(The Sleigh Bell Carol)

At first hearing, this is an enchanting light-hearted carol whose words add greatly to its gaiety. But, on listening to it again, it seems to strike a familiar chord resembling something we know already. It is, in fact, the tune of the Czech carol 'Rocking', sung at twice the speed. What a difference that makes. But we don't need to connect the two carols to be able to enjoy each of them and their own characteristics separately.

Traditional Czech

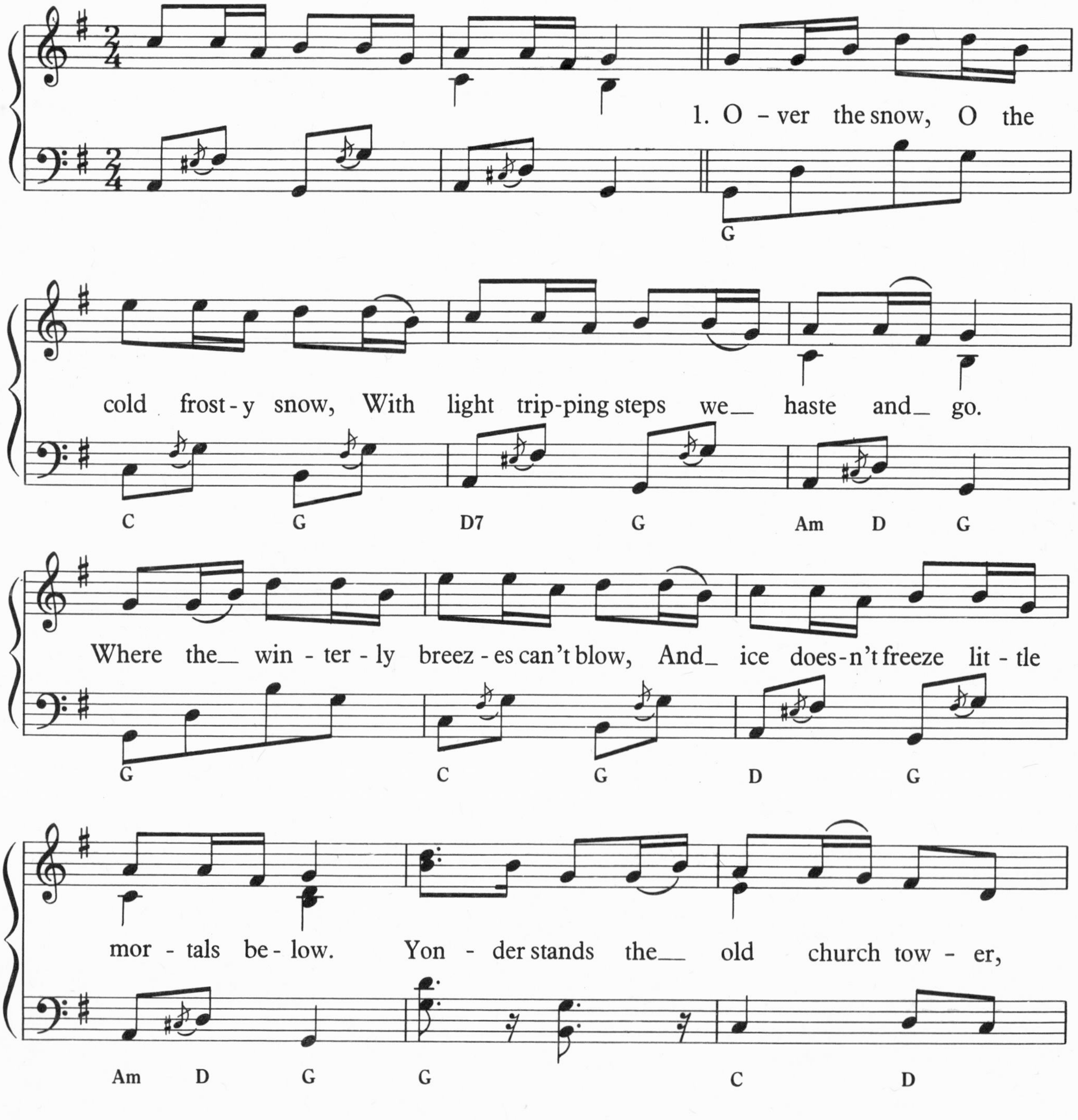

1. O - ver the snow, O the
G
cold frost - y snow, With light trip-ping steps we_ haste and_ go.
C G D7 G Am D G
Where the_ win - ter - ly breez - es can't blow, And_ ice does-n't freeze lit - tle
G C G D G
mor - tals be - low. Yon - der stands the_ old church tow - er,
Am D G G C D

Soon we'll win be - neath its__ shel - ter: Run com-pan - ions__

G   C   D   G

hel - ter__ skel - ter,__ Trot, trot a-long, come trot, come trot a - long.

C   G   D   G   Am   D   G

2. Sing little birds, in the ivy about us,
   Carol your sweetest lay of love,
   While the bells reign in glory above us,
   And the old hymn ev'ry heart straight doth move.
   Sing aloud in praise of Christmas,
   Bells and birds and happy children:
   Hark the gladsome song doth swell,
   As ding dong a ding a dong, goes ev'ry bell.

3. Tra la la la la la la la la la la,
   Tra la la la la la la la la la,
   Tra la la la la la la la la,
   Tra la la la la la la la la la la.
   Sing aloud in praise of Christmas,
   Bells and birds and happy children:
   Little bells like small folk sing;
   And ting, ting a-ling a-ling, their voices ring.

Unto us a Boy is Born

(Puer Nobis)

The words and the music of this splendid carol have come down to us from the 15th century, the verses we use being a translation from the Latin. This was the first new carol I taught the audience at our Town Carol Concert more than forty years ago. It is now becoming better known and singing it gives great satisfaction.

The 2nd and 4th verses can be sung by the ladies. In the third verse the gentlemen can produce some spine chilling tone for 'Herod then with fear was filled'. The last verse calls for full throated voices to make the impact demanded of it . . .

> 'Let the organ thunder,
> While the choir with peals of glee
> Doth rend the air asunder.'

Translation O.B.C.   From the 15th Century German

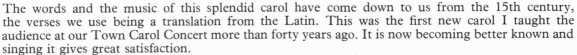

Un - to us a boy is born, King of all cre -

D   A   D   G   D   A7   D   Em7   D   Em   A7

- a - tion: Crad - led in a stall was he, The

D   Bm   A7   A7   Bm   G   A7   D   D7

Lord of ev - 'ry na - tion, The Lord of ev - 'ry na - tion.

G   A   Bm   A   D   G   D   G   A7   D   G   D

2. Cradled in a stall was he
   With sleepy cows and asses;
   But the very beasts could see
   That he all men surpasses.

3. Herod then with fear was filled:
   'A prince', he said, 'in Jewry!'
   All little boys he killed
   At Bethl'em in his fury.

4. Now may Mary's son, who came
   So long ago to love us,
   Lead us all with hearts aflame
   Unto the joys above us.

5. Omega and Alpha he!
   Let the organ thunder,
   While the choir with peals of glee
   Doth rend the air asunder.

Zither Carol

Sir Malcolm Sargent, who did as much in his time to popularise music as any other conductor, loved carols. At his annual carol concert with the Royal Choral Society, he introduced many new ones to his audience, some of which he had arranged himself. For this Zither Carol he also wrote the words.

This Czech folk tune, which I have only come across recently, certainly has zest. It is a rollicking carol to sing and an obvious one for guitars to accompany. Who could resist broadening their shoulders and filling their lungs to join in singing:

'Alleluia the church bells ring,
Alleluia the angels sing,
Alleluia from everything.'?

It is almost revivalist in its feeling—in Sir Malcolm's arrangement the guitar's zing-zing supports the rhythm and finishes each verse with a splendid sweep right across the board.

Malcolm Sargent

Czech Folk Tune

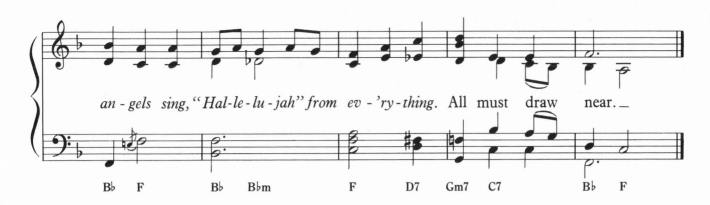

an - gels sing, "Hal-le-lu-jah" from ev-'ry-thing. All must draw near. _

Bb F   Bb Bbm   F   D7 Gm7 C7   Bb F

2. On that day-far away-Jesus lay,
   Angels were watching round his head.
   Holy Child-Mother mild-undefiled,
       We sing thy praise.
       "Hallelujah" etc.
   Our hearts we raise.

3. Shepherds came-at the fame-of thy name,
   Angels their guide to Bethlehem.
   In that place-saw thy face-filled with grace,
       Stood at thy door.
       "Hallelujah" etc.
   Love evermore.

4. Wise men too-haste to do-homage new,
   Gold, myrrh and frankincense they bring.
   As 'twas said-starlight led to thy bed,
       Bending their knee.
       "Hallelujah" etc.
   Worshipping thee.

5. Oh, that we-all might be-good as he,
   Spotless, with God in Unity.
   Saviour dear-ever near-with us here
       Since life began.
       "Hallelujah" etc.
   Godhead made man.

6. Cherubim-Seraphim-worship him,
   Sun, moon and stars proclaim his power.
   Everyday-on our way-we shall say
       Hallelujah,
       "Hallelujah" etc.
   Hallelujah.

Infant Holy

This lovely carol comes from Poland. It needs to be sung simply. The third line uses a short figure repeated each time one note higher to build up the tension of the middle of the carol before relaxing it with a double repeat of the last phrase of the first line. It is ideal for teaching to children or to a mass audience. For four-part choirs there is an admirable arrangement by Edmund Rubbra.

Translation Edith M. Reed

Traditional Polish

It Came Upon the Midnight Clear

This traditional English air is usually sung to the arrangement by Sir Arthur Sullivan. It does not really conform to our definition of a carol, but as a piece of Christmas music it is so splendid and the words so appropriate to our own times that I felt I must include it in this book.

Its message has a universal appeal, which we always underline as we sing:

    'Oh! Listen now, ye men of strife
    And hear the Angels sing.'

Traditional

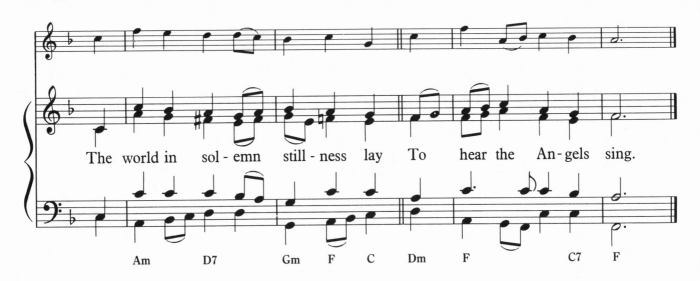

The world in sol-emn still-ness lay To hear the An-gels sing.

Am D7 Gm F C Dm F C7 F

2. Still through the cloven skies they come
    With peaceful wings unfurled;
  And still their heavenly music floats
    O'er all the weary world;
  Above its sad and lowly plains
    They bend on heavenly wing,
  And ever o'er its Babel-sounds
    The blessèd Angels sing.

3. Yet with the woes of sin and strife
    The world has suffered long;
  Beneath the angel-strain have rolled
    Two thousand years of wrong;
  And man, at war with man, hears not
    The words of peace they bring: —
  Oh! listen now, ye men of strife,
    And hear the Angels sing!

4. O Prince of Peace, Thou knowest well
    This weary world below;
  Thou seëst how men climb the way
    With painful steps and slow.
  Oh! still the jarring sounds of earth
    That round the pathway ring,
  And bid the toilers rest awhile
    To hear the Angels sing.

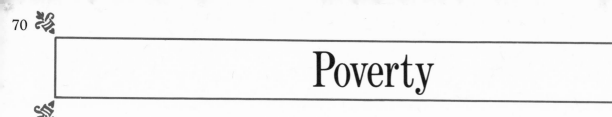

Poverty

Not many carols composed in this century have already passed into the popular repertoire. This Welsh carol, however, is rapidly becoming accepted. For me it expresses all the compassion and fervour of the Welsh people and their great musical traditions.

Translation K. E. Roberts

Dr. Caradog Roberts

1. All poor men and humble, All lame men who stumble, Come
For Jesus, our treasure, With love past all measure, In

col 8va ad lib.

Am D Em D G C G D Em
G

haste ye, nor feel ye afraid; 2. Though wise men who
lowly poor manger was laid. 3. Then haste we to

G C G D11 D7 G G

found him Laid rich gifts around him, Yet oxen they
show him The praises we owe him; Our service he

Am B Em B Em

gave him their hay: And Jesus in beauty Ac-
ne'er can despise: Whose love still is able To

G D G C D Em D

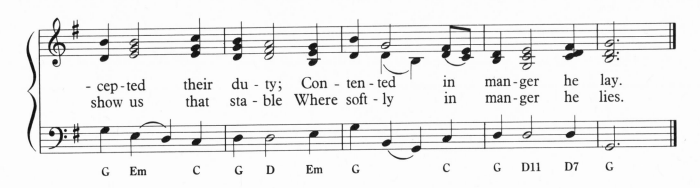

-cep-ted their du-ty; Con-ten-ted in man-ger he lay.
show us that sta-ble Where soft-ly in man-ger he lies.

G Em C G D Em G C G D11 D7 G

Ding Dong! Merrily on High

The words of this carol are set to another old French tune dating from the 16th century. It is natural to emphasise the rhythm of this piece to represent the movement of the bell ringers. The setting of the refrain 'Gloria, Hosanna in excelsis' imaginatively recreates the pealing of the bells ringing out to join the angelic voices in the sky.

G. R. Woodward

From a 16th Century French Carol

Ding dong! mer-ri-ly on high in heav'n the bells are ring - ing:
Ding dong! ve - ri-ly the sky is riv'n with An - gels sing - ing.

Glo - - - - - - - - - - - - - - - - - - - ri - a, Ho - san - na in ex - cel - sis!

2. E'en so here below, below,
   Let steeple bells be swungen,
   And *i-o, i-o, i-o,*
   By priest and people sungen.
   Gloria, Hosanna in excelsis!

3. Pray you, dutifully prime
   Your Matin chime, ye ringers;
   May you beautifully rime
   Your Evetime Song, ye singers:
   Gloria, Hosanna in excelsis!

When Christ was Born of Mary Free

The words of this carol are among the oldest; they appear in a manuscript of 1456. It would be fascinating to have the original music as well but that has been lost.

This tune was written for the almost unchanged words by A. H. Brown and appeared in 1871. There is a marked contrast between the smooth sustained music for the verse and the robust chorus.

15th Century   A. H. Brown

2. Herdsmen beheld these angels bright—
   To them appeared with great light,
   And said 'God's Son is born this night':
   In excelsis gloria.

3. This King is come to save his kind,
   In the scripture as we find;
   Therefore this song have we in mind:
   In excelsis gloria.

4. Then, dear Lord, for thy great grace,
   Grant us in bliss to see thy face,
   Where we may sing to thy solace:
   In excelsis gloria.

Once in Royal David's City

This is a Victorian hymn but it is so much associated with Christmas that I must include it in this book of carols. The words were written by Mrs C. F. Alexander who also wrote 'All things bright and beautiful'. Both were written particularly for children but both now appeal equally to their elders.
There is often a tendency to take this Christmas hymn too fast. It has a simplicity and dignity which needs a measured pace for it to be able to express itself fully.

C. F. Alexander

H. J. Gauntlett

Once in Roy - al Da - vid's ci - ty Stood a low - ly cat - tle shed,

F C F   C F Dm F   Gm C F

Where a mo - ther laid her ba - by In a man - ger for his bed;

F C F   C F   F Dm F   Gm C F

Ma - ry was that mo - ther mild, Je - sus Christ her lit - tle child.

Bb   F Gm C7 F Bb   F Gm C7 F

2. He came down to earth from heaven
   Who is God and Lord of all,
And his shelter was a stable,
   And his cradle was a stall;
With the poor and mean and lowly
Lived on earth our Saviour holy.

3. And through all his wondrous childhood
   He would honour and obey,
Love and watch the lowly Maiden,
   In whose gentle arms he lay:
Christian children all must be,
Mild, obedient, good as he.

4. And our eyes at last shall see him,
   Through his own redeeming love,
For that Child so dear and gentle
   Is our Lord in heaven above;
And he leads his children on
To the place where he is gone.

5. Not in that poor lowly stable,
   With the oxen standing by,
We shall see him; but in heaven,
   Set at God's right hand on high;
Where like stars his children crowned
All in white shall wait around.

Jesus, Jesus, Rest Your Head

I only recently discovered this charming carol, one of ten collected from the Southern Appalachian Mountains in North America. Its charm lies in the simplicity of its tune, the way the melody is phrased in the form of a question to suit the first verse and in the lines:

'All the evil folk on earth
Sleep in feathers at their birth.'

This may or may not be so. What *is* certain is that not everyone who is feather-bedded is evil.

Appalachian Carol collected John Jacob Niles

How His mo - ther went to that sta - ble On that Christ - mas
For the mo - ther and the fa - ther And that bless - ed

Dm C F Bb Gm F Am Bb F Gm F

eve so late? Winds were blow - ing, cows were low - ing,
lit - tle Son; Milk - maids left their fields and flocks

Gm A Dm Bb Dm Gm C7 Dm C F C7

D.C. al Fine

1 **2**

Stars were glow - ing, glow - ing, glow - ing.
And sat be - side the ass and ox.

F Bbmaj7 C F Dm7 G C F Dm7 G C

80

Gloucestershire Wassail

Handed down from singer to singer in Gloucestershire over the last century and a half, this is probably the least well-known of the wassail songs.

Mrs Ralph Vaughan Williams tells me that her husband recorded this carol in August 1908 from an unnamed singer at the inn at Pembridge, Herefordshire. He was there taking down tunes from gypsies in the area for the hop-picking. The singer of 'Wassail Wassail' was not recorded as a gypsy but he may have been a seasonal worker from outside the county who offered it as the 'Gloucestershire' Wassail.

Sung quickly and with good rhythm, this can be a rip-roaring carol. The names Cherry and Dobbin are those of horses, and Broadmay, Fillpail and Collie refer to cows. The lines in the penultimate verse 'But if you do draw us a bowl of small, then down shall go butler, bowl and all' afford a splendid opportunity for musical destruction. The last verse, sung on the tip of the tongue, eagerly anticipates the joys of the buxom wenches and heart-warming hospitality round the fire inside.

Traditional collected Ralph Vaughan Williams

2. So here is to Cherry and to his right cheek,
   Pray God send our master a good piece of beef,
   And a good piece of beef that may we all see;
   With the wassailing bowl we'll drink to thee.

3. And here is to Dobbin and to his right eye,
   Pray God send our master a good Christmas pie,
   And a good Christmas pie that may we all see;
   With our wassailing bowl we'll drink to thee.

4. So here is to Broad May and to her broad horn,
   May God send our Master a good crop of corn.
   And a good crop of corn that may we all see;
   With the wassailing bowl we'll drink to thee.

5. And here is to Fillpail and to her left ear,
   Pray God send our master a happy New Year,
   And a happy New Year as e'er he did see;
   With our wassailing bowl we'll drink to thee.

6. And here is to Colly and to her long tail,
   Pray God send our master he never may fail
   A bowl of strong beer; I pray you draw near,
   And our jolly wassail it's then you shall hear.

7. Come, butler, come fill us a bowl of the best,
   Then we hope that your soul in heaven may rest;
   But if you do draw us a bowl of the small,
   Then down shall go butler, bowl and all.

8. Then here's to the maid in the lily white smock,
   Who tripped to the door and slipped back the lock!
   Who tripped to the door and pulled back the pin,
   For to let these jolly wassailers in.

A Child This Day

This is a West of England traditional carol with a tune of immense vigour. 'Nowell, sing all we may' is the key to its cheerful performance. The phrase 'silly shepherds' has the seventeenth century meaning of 'simple' shepherds.

E. H. Sears

19th Century West of England

2. These tidings shepherds heard,
    In field watching their fold,
 Were by an angel unto them
    That night revealed and told:

Nowell, Nowell, Nowell,
    Nowell, sing all we may,
Because the King of all kings
    Was born this blessed day.

3. To whom the angel spoke,
    Saying, 'Be not afraid;
 Be glad, poor silly shepherds—
    Why are you so dismayed?

4. 'For lo! I bring you tidings
    Of gladness and of mirth,
 Which cometh to all people by
    This holy infant's birth':

5. Then was there with the angel
    An host incontinent
 Of heavenly bright soldiers,
    Which from the Highest was sent:

6. Lauding the Lord our God,
    And his celestial King;
 All glory be in Paradise,
    This heavenly host did sing:

7. And as the angel told them,
    So to them did appear;
 They found the young child, Jesus Christ,
    With Mary, his mother dear:

I Wonder as I Wander

This is another Appalachian carol from North America. The phrasing of the tune matches the wistfulness of the words ending with their childlike declaration of faith:

'He surely could have it
'Cause he was the King'.

Appalachian Carol collected John Jacob Niles

2. When Mary bore Jesus, 'twas in a cow's stall,
   With wise men and farmers and shepherds and all.
   But high from God's heaven a star's light did fall.
   And the promise of ages it then did recall.

3. If Jesus had wanted for any wee thing
   A star in the sky or a bird on the wing,
   Or all of God's angels in heav'n for to sing,
   He surely could have it, for He was the King.

86

I Saw Three Ships

This carol has a wonderful swing about it. It is in fact just like being on a rolling swell at sea. And what fervour the words of the last four verses naturally arouse:

'And all the bells on earth shall ring'
'And all the angels in Heaven shall sing'
'And all the souls on earth shall sing'
'Then let us all rejoice amain!'

As we sing it we should be able to hear in our minds all the bells ringing and all the voices in heaven and on earth singing.

This carol is in all the early broadsheets. It was said to be just as popular and sung as often as 'God Rest You Merry, Gentlemen'. Singing carols all my life by the sea, it obviously has a particular appeal for me.

Traditional

I saw three ships come sail-ing in, On Christ-mas Day, on Christ-mas Day. I saw three ships come sail-ing in, On Christ-mas Day in the morn-ing.

2. And what was in those ships all three?
   On Christmas day. etc.

3. Our Saviour Christ and his lady.
   On Christmas day. etc.

4. Pray, whither sailed those ships all three?
   On Christmas day. etc.

5. O, they sailed into Bethlehem.
   On Christmas day. etc.

6. And all the bells on earth shall ring,
   On Christmas day. etc.

7. And all the angels in Heaven shall sing,
   On Christmas day. etc.

8. And all the souls on earth shall sing.
   On Christmas day. etc.

9. Then let us all rejoice amain!
   On Christmas day. etc.

We Three Kings of Orient Are

I first remember hearing this carol when it was sung in a Nativity play at school just fifty years ago. Being a treble chorister I found myself one of the group of angels who, from an elevated position at the back of the stage, watched the procession of the kings as they came bringing their gifts. In my mind this carol has always been vividly associated with the tall, bearded men from the East, decked out in rich and colourful clothing, whom I saw on that occasion bringing gold, frankincense and myrrh to the stable. All of us gathered round them joined in singing their chorus 'Oh Star of wonder, Star of night, Star with royal beauty bright'.

Even without the pageantry, it is an effective carol. Written in 1857 by Dr J. H. Hopkins in Pennsylvania, U.S.A., it is one of the few examples we have of North American 19th century carols.

John Henry Hopkins

We three kings of O-ri-ent are;
Bear-ing gifts we tra-verse a-far. Field and foun-tain, moor and moun-tain, Fol-low-ing yon-der star: Oh! star of won-der, star of night, Star with roy-al beau-ty bright, West-ward lead-ing,

still pro - ceed - ing, Guide us to thy per - fect light.

C D Bm Em C G Am7 G

2. Born a king on Bethlehem plain,
Gold I bring, to crown him again —
King for ever, ceasing never,
Over us all to reign:

O star of wonder, star of night,
Star with royal beauty bright,
Westward leading, still proceeding,
Guide us to thy perfect light.

3. Frankincense to offer have I;
Incense owns a Deity nigh:
Prayer and praising, all men raising,
Worship him, God most high:

4. Myrrh is mine; its bitter perfume
Breathes a life of gathering gloom;
Sorrowing, sighing, bleeding, dying,
Sealed in the stone-cold tomb:

5. Glorious now, behold him arise,
King, and God, and sacrifice!
Heaven sings alleluya,
Alleluya the earth replies:

Past Three O'Clock

This tune, or at least the refrain, is sometimes referred to as 'The London Waits'. The Watchmen (or Waits), would chant the refrain each hour, on the hour, to reassure the people that they were indeed carrying out their patrol efficiently, and that all was well. Their 'weather reports' were probably useful, also! It is the verses which enable it to be sung as a Christmas carol. These words were added by G. R. Woodward in the 19th century.

G. R. Woodward

Traditional

morn - ing: R℣ Past three - o' - clock; Good mor-row, mas-ters all!

D Em7 D G C Am D G D G

2. ℣. Seraph quire singeth,
Angel bell ringeth:
Hark how they rime it,
Time it, and chime it. R℣

3. ℣. Mid earth rejoices
Hearing such voices
Ne'ertofore só well
Carolling *Nowell*. R℣

4. ℣. Hinds o'er the pearly
Dewy lawn early
Seek the high stranger
Laid in the manger. R℣

5. ℣. Cheese from the dairy
Bring they for Mary,
And, not for money,
Butter and honey. R℣

6. ℣. Light out of star-land
Leadeth from far land
Princes, to meet him,
Worship and greet him. R℣

7. ℣. Myrrh from full coffer,
Incense they offer:
Nor is the golden
Nugget witholden. R℣

8. ℣. Thus they: I pray you,
Up, sirs, nor stay you
Till ye confess him
Likewise, and bless him. R℣

Silent Night

This German carol has established itself over the years as a traditional carol, although, in fact, it was composed by Grüber. The words we use are a translation from the original. It always conjures up a picture of the family singing round the Christmas tree. This reminds us that Christmas trees themselves were an import from Germany which became an integral part of our Christmas festivities about the middle of the last century.

The outstanding merits of this carol are its simplicity and its gentle lilting rhythm.

Anonymous   Franz Grüber

Si - lent night, ho - ly night, all is calm, all is bright;

Round yon Vir - gin and her Child, Ho - ly In - fant so ten-der and mild;

Sleep in hea-ven-ly peace Sleep in hea-ven-ly peace.

2. Silent night, holy night: shepherds quail at the sight;
   Glories stream from heaven afar, heavenly hosts sing alleluia;
   Christ the saviour is born:

3. Silent night, holy night: Son of God, love's pure light;
   Radiant beams thy holy face with the dawn of redeeming grace;
   Jesus, Lord, at thy birth:

O Come, All Ye Faithful

Adeste Fideles, 'O Come All Ye Faithful', provides the most splendid greeting of all for Christmas. When I was carolling as a boy, never a night passed without it being frequently in demand. It thrilled me most, however, when it became the culmination of our three weeks' singing.

On Christmas Eve we used to visit a few houses with big Christmas parties and some hotels where there were large audiences. At 10 o'clock we all returned to our homes so that the ladies could put on long dresses and the gentlemen their dinner jackets. When we emerged we looked much less like carollers, but this was thought to be the only appropriate dress for our final port of call, Kingsgate Castle on the North Foreland. No matter how bleak that windswept point was, illuminated by the light-house flashing out over it, inside the Castle all was warmth and gaiety. At a quarter to midnight we began to sing our carols and as midnight struck we burst into the first verse of 'O Come All Ye Faithful', in which the whole company joined. It was an exciting moment and a fitting climax. Afterwards we mixed with everyone else and enjoyed their hospitality.

Those were the days when Matins was the main service on Christmas day. Now that Midnight Mass is held in our Norman parish church, St Peter-in-Thanet, we have abandoned our earlier traditions and finish carolling in time to go to the church. The service makes its own impact, but it does not have the same dramatic feeling as we all had when we broke into Adeste Fideles at midnight to greet the birth of Christ on Christmas morn.

Translation F. Oakeley

Anonymous 18th Century

O come, all ye faith-ful, Joy-ful and tri-um-phant, O come_ ye, O come_ ye to Beth - le - hem; Come and be-hold Him Born the King of an - gels; O

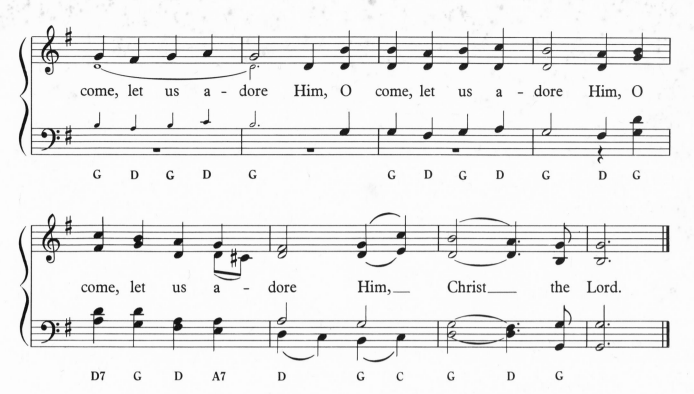

come, let us a - dore Him, O come, let us a - dore Him, O

G D G D G   G D G D G D G

come, let us a - dore Him, ___ Christ ___ the Lord.

D7 G D A7   D   G C G   D G

2. God of God,
Light of light,
Lo! He abhors not the Virgin's womb;
Very God,
Begotten not created;

O come, let us adore Him,
O come, let us adore Him,
O come, let us adore Him,
Christ the Lord.

3. Sing, choirs of angels,
Sing with exultation,
Sing, all ye citizens of heaven above,
Glory to God
In the highest!

4. Yea, Lord, we greet Thee,
Born this happy morning;
Jesu, to Thee be glory given;
Word of the Father,
Now in flesh appearing;